INTRODUCTION

L ong ago, the historic county of Medland was made up of four separate regions. These divisions can now only be found on ancient maps, but people living in the old North, South, East and West Quarters still remain loyal to their own area.

One way that the traditional rivalry between the Quarters is kept up is by means of the County Cup.

Every year, schools from all over the county take part in this great soccer tournament and the standard of football is always high. Matches are played on a local group basis at first to decide the Quarter Champions, who will then clash in the knockout stages of the competition later in the season.

The winners receive the much-prized silver trophy and earn the right to call themselves the County Champions – the top team in Medland.

THE COUNTY OF MEDLAND

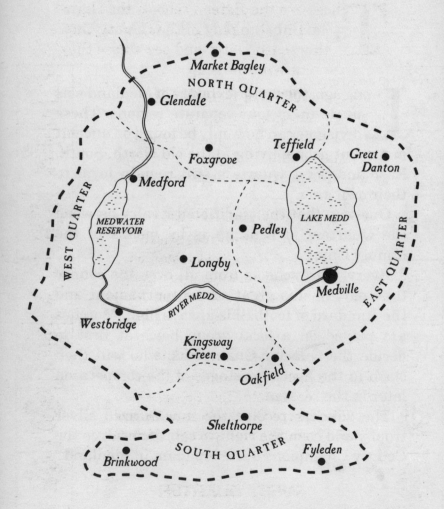

SCHOOLS

These are the sixteen schools that have qualified to play in the County Cup this season – try and see where they are on the map . . .

NORTH QUARTER

Foxgrove High School
Glendale Community School
Market Bagley Community School
Teffield Comprehensive School

EAST QUARTER

Great Danton High School
Lakeview High School, Medville
Medville Comprehensive School
Sir George Needham Community College,
Pedley

SOUTH QUARTER

Fyleden Community College
Oakfield High School
Shelthorpe Comprehensive School
St Wystan's Comprehensive School,
Brinkwood

WEST QUARTER

Hillcrest Comprehensive School, Longby
Kingsway Green High School
Riverside Comprehensive School, Medford
Westbridge Community College

FOXGROVE

GLENDALE

GREAT DANTON

LAKEVIEW

FYLEDEN

OAKFIELD

HILLCREST

KINGSWAY GREEN

MARKET BAGLEY

TEFFIELD

MEDVILLE

SIR GEORGE NEEDHAM

SHELTHORPE

ST WYSTAN'S

RIVERSIDE

WESTBRIDGE

Kingsway Green High School.

Westbridge Community College.

Hillcrest Comprehensive School.

Riverside Comprehensive School.

MEET THE TEAMS

After only a few weeks of the autumn term at their new schools, four teams of under-12 footballers in the West Quarter of Medland will play in the most prestigious soccer tournament for their age-group – the County Cup. As far as they are concerned, it can't start soon enough.

The opening fixtures in the round-robin group are:

**Hillcrest Comprehensive School v
Kingsway Green High School**

**Riverside Comprehensive School v
Westbridge Community College**

Meet the teams on the next few pages and perhaps even choose one that you might like to support in their games. Then follow their fortunes in this book to see what happens in the exciting quest for the County Cup.

Who will be Champions of the West?

Read on and find out . . .

Medium-sized secondary school in the market town of Longby in the West Quarter.

Headteacher: *Mr Gordon Foreman*
Head of P.E. Dept: *Mr Peter Wilson*
School colours: *sky-blue*
Year 7 soccer captain: *Rafiq Chaudhri*
Usual team formation: *4–3–3*

Year 7 soccer squad:

Sam Copeland

Hywel Jenkins	Matthew Denning	Simon Brooke	Amar Ryat
	Rafiq Chaudhri	Scott Gilbert	Ian Wharton
Trevor Miles	Robert (Geoff) Hurst	Barry (Baz) Phillips	

plus: Hussein Sayeed, Mike Allen, Sean Reilly, Tim Norris, Brian Boswell (BB)

CAPTAIN'S Notes...

Our aim this season is to stop Mr Wilson talking about the 'good old days'! It seems the head of the Comp's P.E. department is always going on about the team which won the County Cup ten years ago. In fact, he's already told us newcomers it was the best he's ever had here. Well, we want him to be telling future teams all about us instead.

I really fancy our chances of bringing that silver trophy back to Longby. Most of us played together at the town's main primary school and the Comp's squad has been improved by kids coming from elsewhere, such as defenders Hywel and Hussein, plus strikers Baz and BB.

Who are the other stars? Well, there's me, of course, in midfield! No, not really, but I was dead pleased to be made captain. I tend to do most of my work supporting the defence, leaving people like Scott to push forward and score goals. And we've also got 'Geoff' Hurst leading the attack! Let's hope our Geoff can notch a hat-trick in the County Cup final, just like Sir Geoff did in England's 1966 World Cup victory!

KINGSWAY GREEN HIGH SCHOOL

Small high school in the village of Kingsway Green near the southern boundary of the West Quarter. Pupils in year groups 7, 8 and 9 only, aged between 11 and 14.

Headteacher: *Mr George Taylor*
P.E. teacher: *Mr David Harris*
School colours: *all-purple*
Year 7 soccer captain: *Kyle Richards*
Usual team formation: *4–4–2*

Year 7 soccer squad:

Gary Rees

(Sid)
Harbinder Sidhu   Jon Manning   Max Churchill (Winston)   Jordan Cave

Jack Hodges   Callum Briggs   Amandeep Patel   Aaron Forde

Kyle Richards   Didier Pires (Diddy)

plus: Bradley MacMillan, Hasan Afridi, Connor Stevenson, Joseph Walters, Ben Lynton, Malcolm Douglas

CAPTAIN'S Notes...

We may be a small school but we're the holders of the West Quarter Shield, which is why we're taking part in the County Cup again. Last year's team did incredibly well to win their group against the odds, even though they lost in the semis. They really put Kingsway Green on the soccer map — and we want to keep it there.

We've even signed up a foreign player to help us retain the trophy! My strike-partner, Diddy, comes from France. He's only with us up to Christmas, but he already speaks pretty good English. His favourite word is 'Goal!' Mine too. I was leading scorer for the local primary school.

There's plenty of competition for places in the team. We look to have some good defenders and a lot of skilful ball-players in midfield. Mr Harris is optimistic that the High School is going to have another successful season. Nobody will be taking us lightly, that's for sure.

RIVERSIDE COMPREHENSIVE SCHOOL

Large secondary school in Medford, situated on the River Medd near Medwater Reservoir in the West Quarter.

Headteacher: *Mr Frederick Battersby*
Year 7 soccer coach: *Mr Jeff Riley*
School colours: *red shirts, white shorts and red socks*
Year 7 soccer captain: *David Robson*
Usual team formation: *4–2–4*

Year 7 soccer squad:

Marty Gayle

(Big Norm)
Giles Smith   Chris Wilkins   Adrian Norman   Luke Barton

Lewis Campbell   Paul Illingworth (Illy)

(Buzz)   (Robbo)
Josh Munroe   Joe Aldrin   David Robson   James Rudd

plus: Robert McDonald, Thomas Armstrong, George Perkins, Neil Bailey, Gregg Lightfoot, Alex Clough, Anand Modi

We're sure to be the group's high fliers. With people like Armstrong and Aldrin around, you could say we'll be feeling over the moon if we win the County Cup!

Did you spot those two famous astronauts' names in our squad? Mr Riley keeps making weak jokes like mine in practice sessions, telling them to get into space and try some rocket shots etc. Bet they're getting fed up of it already. 'Buzz' has had that nickname for years, but he and Tom didn't even know each other till they came here.

Mr Riley runs the West Quarter side too and included a lot of his own school squad in the recent area trials so he must rate our chances this season. It's amazing to have so many players in one team who are natural left-footers like me. (There's also Big Norm, Luke, Illy, James and Tom.) It proved quite an advantage in our first couple of games – won them both dead easy.

Looks like you'd better come to Riverside if you want to see all the stars!

15

WESTBRIDGE COMMUNITY COLLEGE

L arge comprehensive school in the town of Westbridge on the River Medd in the West Quarter.

Headteacher: *Mr Walter Hooper*
P.E. teacher: *Mr Doug Griffiths*
School colours: *white shirts, black shorts and socks*
Year 7 soccer captain: *Emerson Marshall*
Usual team formation: *4–1–3–2 (attacking sweeper system)*

Year 7 soccer squad:

Adam Trent			
Dan Cross	Emerson Marshall	Brad Gibson	Craig Dalton
	William Kennedy (Kenny)		
Eddie Atkins	Richard (King Kong) Congdon	Yagnesh Sharma	
	Iain Baxter (Bax)	Sam Lucas	

plus: Mark Palmer, Ajay Jethwa, Jacob Roberts, (Bob) Dylan Small, Jim Chalmers, Dean Matthews, Andy Thornton

CAPTAIN'S Notes...

Not exactly the greatest of starts to the football season at the College. They've just finished building a sports hall here and the playing fields have been churned up into a right mess by all the heavy vehicles. Only one of the soccer pitches has escaped damage, but it's miles too big for us first-years.

We've only been able to practise in the old gym so far and Mr Griffiths seems to spend half the time checking our names. Mind you, he must have spotted some talent. He took six of us to the area trials and four have made the Quarter squad – me, Dan, Kenny and Adam.

We used a kind of sweeper system in our first league game, a 2–1 away win, when Kenny played in this 'libero' role, as Mr Griffiths calls it. I think it means the 'free man'. Kenny scored, anyway, but it was a good job Adam had a blinder in goal.

Just hope we get the pitches fit soon or we might have to play all our matches away from home this season, even in the County Cup!

EN ROUTE

. . . before the County Cup gets underway, here's an early chance to check out the form of the best players from all the competing schools. Let's hitch a lift with some of the Westbridge footballers as they travel to Medford to play in their first area match for the West Quarter . . .

'Who's Quarter captain, Mr Griffiths, do you know?'

The boy tried to make it sound like a casual enquiry, gazing out of the rain-splattered car window at the view of the reservoir. The driver smiled, guessing how much the answer really did matter to his school team captain.

'I'm afraid I haven't heard anything, Emerson,' he replied, 'but if Mr Riley had chosen one of you people, I'm sure he would have told me.'

'Oh . . .' There was a definite tinge of disappointment in the response. 'Just wondering, that's all.'

'Tough luck, Emerson,' came a snigger from the back seat. 'You can't always be captain, y'know.'

Emerson Marshall turned and glared at Dan.

'I wasn't expecting to be. It could have been you for all I care.'

'Huh! Fat chance!'

Mr Griffiths glanced in his rear-view mirror and saw Dan's scowling face. The Westbridge teacher hadn't yet had much time to get to know his new squad of players, but so far he had seen little to admire about this particular boy – apart from his footballing ability. 'Why's that, Dan?' he asked.

'Well, to quote my old teacher at the primary school: "You're not exactly captaincy material, are you, Daniel Cross?" I think those were his words.'

'And what were his reasons for saying that to you?'

Dan shrugged. 'Well, it might've had something to do with the fact that I'd just thumped one of my own teammates,' he said and then smirked at the other two boys sitting next to him. 'During a match!'

'What had he done?' gasped Adam, their goalkeeper. 'Scored an own goal or something?'

'Nothing like that,' grinned Kenny. 'If I remember right, Dan's excuse was that this kid hadn't passed the ball to him when he called for it.'

19

Dan made no attempt to deny the tale. 'Just wish I hadn't hit him so hard,' he added. 'Bust one of my own fingers as well as his nose!'

The three backseat footballers convulsed into laughter and Mr Griffiths exchanged a raised eyebrow with Emerson before concentrating once more on his driving. Leaving Medwater Reservoir behind them, he soon reached the large village of Medford and pulled into the car park of Riverside Comprehensive School. It was now raining quite heavily.

'OK, lads, enjoy the game, despite the weather,' he said. 'It's a great honour to represent your Quarter. Play well and good luck.'

As they climbed out of the car, the area team manager greeted them warmly. 'It's always a relief to see my referee turn up,' he smiled, shaking Mr Griffiths by the hand. 'And my stars too, of course. Not seen you all since the trials so let's see if I can still put names to faces – Emerson, Adam, er . . . Kenny, isn't it? Right – and . . . er . . .'

'Dan,' said the defender, jerking down the hood of his coat.

'Right – sorry, Dan,' said Mr Riley. 'Follow me, lads, and I'll show you where to change. The East party hasn't arrived yet, so there's no rush.'

Kenny nudged Dan on the arm as they trailed after him. 'You've obviously made a big impression on the coach,' he teased.

'Huh! Typical, that is. Well, I'll make sure Riley doesn't forget my name again after this match.'

'Just so long as you don't go thumping anybody,' Emerson butted in. 'We don't want to have to play with only ten men.'

'Griff wouldn't dare send me off,' Dan sneered. 'I reckon he's a bit of a wimp. We'll be able to get away with murder this season.'

'Murder must be a red card offence,' chuckled Adam. 'Even for Griff!'

J91, 895

WEST v EAST

Thursday 2 October
k.o. 4.30 p.m.
Referee: Mr D. Griffiths

. . . it only takes Dan Cross five minutes to make his mark on the game – and on the left-winger's ankle . . .

The East Quarter's number eleven had made the mistake of deciding to nutmeg Dan the very first time they confronted one another. As he slipped the ball through the full-back's legs and attempted to run past him on the outside, a set of raised studs abruptly halted his progress.

Roars of protest went up from the visiting supporters on the touchline as the referee blew for a foul. Dan pretended to show concern for his victim, bending over him while he writhed on the wet ground.

'Try and do anything like that again and I'll break your leg next time,' he snarled into the boy's ear.

Mr Griffiths took Dan to one side as the winger received some first aid on the pitch. 'That was a nasty foul, Dan,' he said sternly.

'It was accidental – didn't mean to catch him, honest.'

'Not the way I saw it. Just be careful, OK?'

Dan turned away to conceal his smirk, but then Emerson had a go at him too. 'Cool it, you idiot – or you *will* get yourself sent off.'

'Belt up. You're not captain here so don't try and boss me around.'

Mr Riley's choice was his own Riverside captain, and it was David Robson who struck first to give West the lead ten minutes into the game. He was put through on goal by his Hillcrest counterpart, Rafiq Chaudhri, and he finished in style, lashing his left-footed shot high into the roof of the net.

Rafiq was the first player to catch up with the

scorer as he ran towards the corner flag in celebration. 'Great goal, Robbo!' he whooped. 'Sensational!'

The East goalkeeper stared in disgust at his defenders. He took any goal he let in as a personal insult. 'Sort out the marking,' he yelled angrily, jabbing a finger at the culprits. 'You just stood and watched that guy shoot.'

The extrovert, loud-mouthed keeper proved to be the dominant figure – and voice – of the first half. The football traffic in the pouring rain might well have been almost entirely one-way towards East's goal, but the attackers could find no other route past his watertight roadblock.

'Unbelievable that the score's only one–nil!' exclaimed Mr Riley at half-time. 'Well, you've got your work cut out now, lads, that's for sure. The wind and rain will be in your faces second half. Let's see what you're made of.'

The manager had a private word of warning with Dan as the players took the field again. 'I've seen what's been going on, even if the ref hasn't spotted everything. You must have kicked that winger more than the ball.'

The boy shrugged. 'Had no trouble from him, have we?' he retorted cheekily. 'He knows he's got to give me a wide berth.'

'That's not the point. One more bad foul and I'll sub you, understand?'

In fact Dan found himself up against a different opponent in the second half, a bigger, stronger boy who was not one to shy away from a tackle. Their first encounter was like a collision of juggernauts. It left both of them sitting in a puddle, forcing grins to try and hide their pain.

As anticipated, East gained the upper hand now that conditions were more in their favour and it was the new winger who set up a deserved equalizer. He was half-tripped by Dan just outside the penalty area but somehow kept his feet and pulled the ball back across the goal-mouth. The fierce, close-range strike gave Adam no chance of making a save.

'Right, you've had it now, kid,' muttered Dan under his breath. 'I'll get you for that.'

East piled on the pressure in a determined bid for victory, but Emerson was having an out-standing game in central defence. It was usually his crucial tackle or block that rescued his team whenever danger threatened, although Adam also showed why he was the West Quarter's number-one goalkeeper. One brilliant, acrobatic tip over the bar was quite breathtaking.

Then Dan decided that the time had come to seek his revenge. In a crowded goal area, as players milled about before a corner came over, he aimed a vicious kick at the back of the winger's legs and the boy crumpled into the mud. Adam leapt to catch the slippery ball cleanly and booted it upfield as the East players appealed for a penalty.

The referee hadn't seen the incident and waved play-on, but Mr Riley was in no doubt about what had happened. 'Right, Dan, off!' he called out, signalling that he wanted to make a substitution. 'Take over at full-back, please, Kenny.'

'Why have I come off?' demanded Dan, pulling on his tracksuit top.

'You know full well why,' snapped the manager. 'I don't want anybody playing for the West acting like that. What you did there was disgraceful.'

'Well, I don't want to play for you either,' Dan scowled and stormed off to get his coat, leaving the manager fuming.

Mr Riley was only cheered up by seeing his team grab a winning goal against the run of play right near the end of the game. East were caught on the break when Kenny burst out of defence up the right touchline and lofted over a centre that put Riverside's 'Buzz' Aldrin in the clear.

The goalkeeper came off his line quickly to dive at the striker's feet and smother the ball, but it squirmed out of his grasp. Following up close behind was the Kingsway Green captain, Kyle Richards, and he calmly tucked the loose ball into the net.

After the final whistle the manager walked to the changing room with the referee. Their school sides would be meeting on this same ground the following week in the County Cup.

'I hope you can talk some sense into that Dan before our Cup game,' said Mr Riley. 'If he goes round kicking my players up in the air, he's going to be in serious trouble with me.'

Mr Griffiths was grim-faced. 'The boy's got a real attitude problem, I'm afraid. He's well named all right.'

'How do you mean?'

'Cross by name, cross by nature, it seems,' he replied. 'I shall have to make it clear to him what kind of behaviour we expect at Westbridge College.'

Dan and Mr Griffiths had nothing to say to each other in the car. It was a very quiet return journey home.

. . . both the opening County Cup games are scheduled for the same day so before the clash between Riverside and Westbridge, let's first see the highlights of the match at Longby . . .

HILLCREST v KINGSWAY GREEN

Wednesday 8 October
k.o. 4.15 p.m.
Referee: Mr P. Wilson

. . . no goals yet, midway through the first half, but Hillcrest are putting the Shield holders under increasing pressure . . .

The corner kick caused a frenzied scramble in the Kingsway Green goalmouth. The ball was twice kicked off the line before it spun loose to the Sky-Blues' leading scorer, 'Geoff' Hurst.

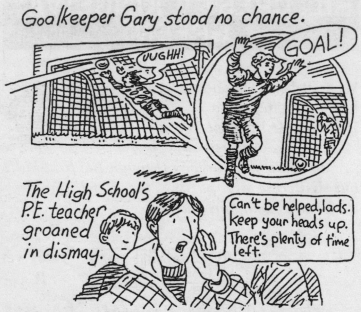

Mr Harris could only hope that his players might be able to survive until half-time without conceding another goal. They did, just, thanks to some superb saves from Gary.

Half-time.

Let's give their keeper some work to do as well. He hasn't even got his knees dirty yet. Try and get the ball up to Kyle and Didier more quickly. Bonne chance!

The second half was much more evenly balanced. Gary was still kept busy, but his team also did their fair share of attacking. Captain Kyle and his French strike-partner both went close to scoring.

Didier's skilful chip scraped the top of the crossbar.

Great effort, Diddy.

Merci Kyle. Quel dommage!

Whatever you say, pal. Just get the next one a bit lower, OK?

It was third time lucky for the holders.
Five minutes later Kyle's cross found
Didier unmarked in front of goal.

The teacher was being optimistic. As it turned out, neither side could produce a winning goal and they had to settle for a point apiece. After the final whistle Mr Harris shook hands with the referee.

. . . bet you want to know the answer to that question, too, so let's switch straight over to Medford and find out . . .

RIVERSIDE v WESTBRIDGE

Wednesday 8 October
k.o. 4.15 p.m.
Referee: Mr J. Riley

. . . shortly before the kick-off, Mr Riley takes the chance to check with his Westbridge colleague about Dan Cross . . .

'I trust that Dan knows I won't stand any nonsense from him today on the pitch,' said the Riverside referee. 'Nor take any more of his lip.'

'Well, I've tried to stress how important it is to play the game in the right spirit, but it's not easy getting through to that boy,' sighed Mr Griffiths. 'In fact it's not even easy finding him at school. He's been known to turn up for registration and then bunk off.'

Mr Riley nodded. 'Right, so we can add truancy to his growing list of crimes, can we?' he said wearily.

'Don't write him off completely yet, Jeff. Let's just see how he responds, OK?'

Both teachers were relieved to see that Dan appeared to be on his best behaviour. He had a brilliant first half. The full-back was tremendous in defence early on when the home side launched wave after wave of attacks, and later played a key part in the visitors' retaliation.

Winning possession – with a fair tackle – just outside his own penalty area, Dan produced an impressive turn of speed over the halfway line before suddenly hitting the ball out to the opposite flank. His clever switch found Yagnesh Sharma in oceans of space and the left-footed midfielder scored with a low, twenty-metre drive.

There were many players on view who had been involved in the Quarter trials during September, but Yagnesh had not been one of them. Mr Riley regretted the goal against his own school team, but looked at the slimly built Asian lad with interest as Westbridge celebrated. He had to be impressed with the quality of such a strike.

'Where have you been hiding *him*?' the referee said to Mr Griffiths as he jogged by for the restart.

'Sorry, I'm only just realizing how good he is myself,' came the grinning reply. 'Not seen all that much of him yet – y'know, with our pitches being out of action like they are.'

There were no further goals before half-time. The strong Westbridge defence, well organized by captain Emerson and sweeper Kenny, had so far managed to cancel out the dangerous Riverside attack led by Robbo and Buzz. Quarter team friendships were put on hold for the sake of school rivalries and County Cup points.

It was well into the second period before the match exploded into life – and Dan's short, fast-burning fuse was also ignited.

In a hectic, five-minute spell, Riverside's 0–1 deficit was transformed into a 2–1 lead. After

Buzz scored with a volley that not even Quarter goalkeeper Adam Trent could stop, he then had to be carried off the pitch with a long gash down his right leg.

The disappointment of the equalizer had proved too much for Dan's fragile temperament. He took his anger out on the striker with a wild, high lunge inside the area that should have earned Westbridge a double punishment – a penalty and the disadvantage of being reduced to ten players.

The penalty was given, of course, but an earlier agreement between the teachers spared Dan the disgrace of being sent off. He was immediately subbed again instead. The boy's clearly audible cursing as he stomped away did not help his cause and Mr Griffiths left him to cool off by himself on the touchline. He didn't much fancy a public confrontation.

Robbo had the satisfaction of sending Adam the wrong way with his well-placed penalty kick, but that was almost the last thing the Riverside captain had to smile about. He missed a good chance to give his team a two-goal advantage by lobbing the ball over the bar and then had to watch helplessly as Westbridge snatched an equalizer.

'Push forward more, Kenny,' Emerson told his sweeper. 'No good staying back now we're losing.'

There was nothing Kenny loved more than joining in any attacks. He soon linked up with Yagnesh near the left touchline and steered a pass between Riverside's two big central defenders for Iain Baxter to dribble the ball round the goalkeeper and roll it into the empty net.

'Great goal, Bax!' Kenny whooped, jumping onto the scorer's back. 'I couldn't have done it better myself.'

Bax laughed. 'Bet you'd have made a complete mess of it – tripped up over your own feet or something.'

'Rubbish! I scored more goals than you last season, remember.'

'Well played, lads,' Mr Griffiths called out from close by. 'Back in defence now, though, Kenny. We don't want to let them score again.'

The last few minutes were nervous ones. Both teams wanted badly to win and claim all three points, but could not afford to risk losing. Defences were tightened up and neither goalkeeper was seriously troubled.

Straight after the match, Mr Riley strode across to catch Dan before he reached the school changing room. 'Wait a minute, I want a word with you, young man,' he began. 'That's twice in two matches you've let yourself down – and that's twice too many as far as I'm concerned. What Mr Griffiths decides to do is up to him, but I shan't be picking you for the Quarter again.'

Dan shrugged. 'Don't bother me,' he replied in a surly manner. 'I'd rather go midweek training with my Sunday team, anyway.'

That was the end of one boy's brief representative career.

. . . wonder how you'd get on with a character like Dan if he were in your team? . . .

CUP STATS AND FIXTURES

Opening Games

Result:	Hillcrest 1 v 1	Kingsway Green
	h-t: 1 – 0	
Scorers:	Hurst	Pires

Result:	Riverside 2 v 2	Westbridge
	h-t: 0 – 1	
Scorers:	Aldrin	Sharma
	Robson (pen)	Baxter

Remaining group matches (to be played on the specified dates):

Saturday 8 November
Westbridge v Hillcrest
Kingsway Green v Riverside

Saturday 6 December
Hillcrest v Riverside
Kingsway Green v Westbridge

. . . *with the opening group games drawn, all schools are off the mark with one point apiece. Looking at the fixtures to come, the holders Kingsway Green seem well placed with both their matches at home, whereas Riverside are now faced with two away games. And remember that Westbridge have pitch problems. How much of an advantage might it be, do you think, to play at home at this age? . . .*

BALL SKILLS

. . . let's join in Kingsway Green's first practice session after half-term to see the players working on their skills in the hope of retaining the Quarter Shield . . .

'Try and receive the ball sideways on, Callum, so you can see who's around you,' advised Mr Harris. 'Too often, you're having to trap it then turn and look up. Wastes time.'

The teacher did most of his coaching in the square training grids marked out near the school building. At the moment, playing on pitches just two grids long, teams of three were attempting to pass a ball from one end to the other without their opponents taking it off them. Ball control had to be quick and tight in the restricted space.

'Screen the ball, Jack, hold it, keep sideways on, that's good,' he encouraged. 'Well done – now Callum's free – give it and go.'

Jack gave it and went. He knocked the ball into Callum's path and then sprinted for the return pass. The one-two exchange was perfect and Jack was sent clear to dribble the ball over the far line to earn his side a point.

Mr Harris had coached last year's squad to their Shield triumph and was hopeful of repeating that success this season, even though he knew it was going to be a tough task. The other teams in the group were packed with area players, whereas only his captain had made the West's starting line-up in their recent draw with the North.

Kyle Richards was on the ball now, drawing an opponent towards him before slipping it to Didier on the left of the grid. Their French import killed the ball with his instep and turned away from his marker in one swift movement. The teacher almost purred in delight at such skills, especially when Didier tricked everyone with a well-disguised backheel pass.

Well, nearly everyone. Only Kyle had read his intentions and scampered off with the ball to score an extra point. The two strikers were developing a good relationship on and off the field and they jumped up to slap each other's raised hand in fun.

41

'Pity you're leaving us at Christmas, Diddy,' said Kyle. 'Just think what we'd do if we had a whole season together.'

Didier picked up the gist of the captain's gabbled sentiments and smiled. 'We are thinking, *peut-être*, on the same ... um ... roads, *oui*?'

Kyle grinned. 'Yeah, on the same lines, right. We're on the same wavelength, you and me.'

'Wavelength?'

'Yeah, I've no idea what the French is for that. Who needs words when we've got a better understanding with the ball, eh?'

Didier looked blank, but was happy that Kyle seemed pleased with him. They paired up as partners when Mr Harris next had the players passing to one another across the grids. As they showed him that they could control the ball well enough over short distances, he allowed them to move back and do longer, higher passes to practise taking the ball on their chest or thigh.

'Cushion the impact,' he told them. 'I don't want to see it bouncing off anybody like a wall. Wherever it hits you, relax that part – make it soft – and drop the ball down to your feet.'

Mr Harris didn't even see the ball coming. Callum's wayward pass flew well wide of his partner Jack but was deadly accurate in finding the teacher. All the players heard the loud grunt and turned to see their coach crumpling to the ground in pain.

'What happened?' cried Kyle.

Jack was trying to stop himself from giggling too loudly. 'Callum's just found Mr Harris's soft parts,' he choked. 'Cushioned it great!'

'Reckon he should've been more sideways on,' cackled Callum.

. . . what's your ball control like? While Mr Harris is struggling to find his breath, listen to what the County Coach has to say on the subject . . .

BALL CONTROL

If you can control a ball quickly, you then have more time and space to run with it, pass or shoot.

Want to improve your own ball control skills? Take a few tips from me.

✓ Relax body-part upon impact to cushion the ball – draw it in
✓ If body-part is kept firm, the ball will rebound away
✓ Keep your eyes on the ball as it arrives
✓ Move into line of pass quickly to get body right behind ball
✓ Using feet: trap ball between inside of boot and the ground
✓ Sole or instep can be used too, needing extra skill
✓ Using chest: puff out chest, then relax and bring shoulders forward
✓ Using thigh: raise, then drop knee on impact to cushion ball to feet
✓ Cushion headers too to drop ball at own feet or teammate's
✓ Keep practising

HOLD IT!

BANNED

. . . meanwhile, over at Westbridge, problems are mounting . . .

Mr Griffiths sat in the changing room after morning assembly and read the letter that Mr Hooper, the headteacher, had just passed on to him. It informed the College that one of their pupils, Dan Cross, had recently been sent off in a Sunday League game for 'foul play and verbal abuse of a referee'.

'Only a matter of time,' sighed the teacher, shaking his head. He had almost

> nave, regrettably na
> itter and must notify
> ll be suspended for a
> im playing football fo

been waiting for this to happen. The three-week suspension notified in the letter banned Dan from playing not just for Westbridge Wanderers, but also for any other team during that period.

By coincidence, Dan's class arrived for a P.E. lesson at that moment, but he didn't seem to be among the group that clattered noisily into the room.

'Where's Dan Cross?' asked Mr Griffiths, raising his voice above the babble. The boys became strangely quiet all of a sudden, trying to look engrossed in the business of changing. 'Is he away again?'

Nobody answered and the teacher's suspicions were immediately aroused. 'Stay in here, all of you. Don't move,' he ordered and ran outside into the rain. Instinctively, he turned left past the new sports hall and stared across the water-logged playing fields.

At first there was no sign of anybody, but then something caught his eye in the distance. It was a figure moving furtively, half-crouched, along the public footpath that skirted the school grounds towards a housing estate. Mr Griffiths had a gut feeling that he knew just who that figure might be.

Without hesitating, he squelched across the first football pitch, but had only gone thirty metres when he tripped over a deep rut and went sprawling full-length. He used language he wouldn't have tolerated from any of the children and picked himself up to examine the state of his tracksuit.

'Right, if it comes to a chase,' he muttered, 'there's no way that kid is going to get away from me now.'

Dan was almost on the edge of the estate before he became aware that somebody was in pursuit. And when he realized who it was, he knew there was no point in trying to outrun his own P.E. teacher. He simply carried on walking, hoping to appear nonchalant, until he heard Mr Griffiths approach.

'Just where do you think you're going?' came the bellow behind him.

'Home, Mr Griffiths. Forgot my P.E. kit so I was just nipping back to fetch it.'

Mr Griffiths panted to a halt, still fuming from his fall. 'Who gave you permission to go home?' he demanded fiercely.

'Er, nobody,' Dan answered, deciding a form of the truth was his best policy. He had never seen Mr Griffiths look so angry.

'You know you're not allowed to leave school without permission – and you also know we've got spare kit for people with bad memories.'

'Yeah, but it's filthy,' the boy replied cheekily, deliberately eyeing the teacher's mud-stained tracksuit. 'Not as bad as yours, though.'

'I did this coming after you. So you live on this estate, do you?'

'Well, close by. Just thought it might be a bit of a shortcut, like.'

'I bet you did. The quickest way to skip school. Don't you think you're in enough trouble already without playing truant as well?' said Mr Griffiths, brandishing the letter that he was still holding. 'We've just heard about your soccer ban. You never told me you'd been sent off on a Sunday.'

'Didn't think it was any of the school's business.'

'Well, it is. And do you know why it is, lad? Because it means you're banned from playing for us too. You're going to miss our next Cup match.'

The news appeared to come as a shock to Dan. For a moment the colour drained from his face. 'They can't do that.'

'Oh yes, they can. I wonder what your team-mates are going to say when they find out, eh?'  he said, pausing briefly to let that uncomfortable thought sink in before continuing. 'Come on, back with me, and let's have no more of this charade. I think Mr Hooper will be wanting to speak to you first about a few matters concerning your behaviour – in and out of school.'

Dan made no protest. He trailed along the

footpath towards the school, pulling his hood over his face to keep off the rain. He also didn't want the teacher to see the tears in his eyes.

. . . *Dan might well be in hot water, but the Westbridge soccer pitches are soon underwater – within a week the heavy rain has caused the River Medd to burst its banks and flood the surrounding area, including the College playing fields . . .*

HILLCREST v WESTBRIDGE

Saturday 8 November
k.o. 10 a.m.
Referee: Mr P. Wilson

*. . . the footballers feared it might be a case of
'rain stopped play', but it takes more than a bit of
local flooding to halt the County Cup – the game
is switched to higher ground at Longby . . .*

Dan was not the only player missing from the
Westbridge party that splashed out of town in a
convoy of cars and drove up into the West
Quarter hills. Leading scorer Iain Baxter was
also absent through illness.

'I hope Bob will do OK for us up front today,'
Emerson said to his father as they discussed the
team. 'Dan's been saying all week we're going to
lose without him and Bax.'

'What nonsense! I reckon you're better off
without all his fouling,' replied Mr Marshall.
'Who is this Bob, anyway?'

'Well, his real name is Dylan Small, but he
gets called after that old singer, y'know.'

'Sure do, son. I was a big fan of Bob Dylan once.'

Mr Marshall burst into the chorus of his favourite Dylan song, *Blowin' in the Wind*, and might have continued all the way to Longby if Emerson hadn't pleaded with him to shut up.

They were greeted on arrival by the Hillcrest captain, Rafiq, and the two Quarter teammates went to inspect the pitch together. 'It's amazing you've just got a few puddles here in the goal-mouths,' said Emerson. 'Reckon about the only game we could have played at Westbridge is water polo!'

'I half wish we were flooded too and then the match could have been postponed,' Rafiq moaned. 'Three of our regulars have gone down with flu.'

'Things could be worse,' Emerson grinned. 'At least Dan's not around today either to break any bones.'

Hillcrest's stand-in striker, Brian Boswell, getting his chance in the team because of the flu outbreak, was also glad to hear that piece of news. Before moving to Longby he had been at the same primary school as Dan and many of the Westbridge players. Everyone knew him as BB.

And it was BB, to his own astonishment and

huge delight, who had the honour of opening the scoring against his old classmates. Centre-forward Geoff Hurst unselfishly laid the ball into his path when he might have tried a shot himself and BB bulged the net from close range. The goal served as a small token of consolation for his misshapen nose.

Emerson ensured that his team learnt its lessons from that early setback. The opposing attackers never enjoyed so much freedom again, especially while Kenny concentrated more on defensive duties instead of marauding upfield. He'd been caught hopelessly out of position for the goal, a fact that Mr Griffiths was not slow to remind the sweeper about at half-time.

By then, the scores were level and the visitors were beginning to dominate the game. Mid-fielder Richard Congdon, King Kong to his mates, had equalized from Yagnesh's pass, and both Yagnesh and Bob had narrowly failed to shoot Westbridge ahead.

'You're well on top now,' Mr Griffiths told his players. 'If you can put those kind of chances away second half, you should be able to win this.'

The mood in the home camp was much less positive. 'Just keep doing your best and hope for a bit of luck,' said their teacher, Mr Wilson.

'They're not unbeatable – not a patch on that great team of mine ten years ago. We'd have wiped the floor with this Westbridge lot then, no trouble.'

'C'mon, men,' urged Rafiq as they lined up again. 'This is our chance to show Willy how good we really are. If we can get a result here, he might even start believing he's got another Cup-winning team on his hands.'

They were brave words, but even Rafiq began to doubt if it was going to be their day when Lady Luck smiled on Westbridge instead only three minutes into the half. The goal was a fluke. The visitors' number ten, Sam Lucas, sliced his shot but saw it take a deflection off a defender's shoulder, flip up against the bar, then ricochet down and hit the goalie on the head before rolling into the net. The boy had dived in vain for the original effort and was still lying in the mud when the ball bounced off him.

Hillcrest fought back hard, but they badly missed the driving force of Scott Gilbert in midfield, one of the flu victims. Scott was the engine room of the team and he also had a good eye for goal. And goal-power was what they were lacking, especially with top scorer Geoff looking a bit off colour too. Their best chance fell to BB, but this time his rising shot was acrobatically pushed over the bar by area keeper Adam Trent.

A minute later Westbridge broke away to score again and the match was as good as settled. Kenny, King Kong, Yagnesh and Sam all linked up in a flowing move up the left, with Sam's final shot only partly parried by his name-sake in the Hillcrest goal. The ball might even have bobbled into the net, but Dylan Small followed up to make sure by tapping it over the line.

'You could've left it, Bob,' Sam complained. 'The ball was going in, anyway.'

'Soz, Sam,' he smirked in reply. 'You've already claimed that other dodgy goal. This one's mine.'

There was no way back for Hillcrest after that. Emerson insisted that Westbridge continued to defend in numbers, snuffing out any chance of a Hillcrest revival.

'Proud of you, son, well played today,' his father said in praise on the return journey. 'You're not far off making those Cup semis now. As old Bob Dylan put it, you're *Knockin' on Heaven's Door* . . .'

The car was soon resounding to Mr Marshall's deep baritone voice and Emerson clamped his hands over his ears in mock horror, begging for mercy.

Result:	Hillcrest 1 v 3 Westbridge	
	h-t: 1 – 1	
Scorers:	Boswell	Congdon, Lucas Small

. . . Kingsway Green and Riverside were also in action that morning, of course – let's find out who else is now hammering on that door into the semis . . .

KINGSWAY GREEN v RIVERSIDE

. . . Buzz Aldrin's task after being named 'Man of the Match' by Mr Riley was to write a report on the game for the weekly school magazine – this is how it appeared the following Friday . . .

The *Riverside Review*

Year 7 Team in Cup Thriller

Reporter: Joe 'Buzz' Aldrin

With the River Medd almost lapping up to the school gates last Saturday, it was a good job our County Cup game against the Quarter Shield holders was away from home.

We got off to a fantastic start and led 2–0 at half-time, with goals from me and Big Norm, our centre-back. My goal was set up by an amazing dribble by captain Robbo and then Big Norm zonked in a header from a corner that nearly burst the net.

Kingsway Green fought back well in the second

half. They had a really purple patch to match the colour of their kit and blitzed us for about ten minutes, scoring twice themselves. Some kid who was yabbering away in French all match got their first goal and the equalizer was scored by Kyle, their captain.

We were in real trouble for a while, but fortunately I soon managed to put us back in the lead. One of their defenders slipped and left me in the clear with only the keeper to beat. I dribbled round him and it was a great feeling to smash the ball into the net for what proved to be the winning goal.

Everything now depends on our last game next month to see if we can top the group and qualify for the semis. The Comp for the Cup!

Final result:
Riverside 3
Kingsway Green 2

Result:	Kingsway Green	2 v 3	Riverside
		h-t: 0- 2	
Scorers:	Pires		Aldrin (2)
	Richards		Norman

GROUP TABLE

	P	W	D	L	Goals F	A	(GD)	Pts
Westbridge	2	1	1	0	5	3	(+2)	4
Riverside	2	1	1	0	5	4	(+1)	4
Kingsway Green	2	0	1	1	3	4	(−1)	1
Hillcrest	2	0	1	1	2	4	(−2)	1

Analysis

With the bottom two teams playing the top two in the last set of games, all four schools have a chance of winning the group and qualifying for the semi-final stage of the County Cup. Goal difference (GD) might become very important. It's possible, depending upon results, that every school could finish with four points, perhaps needing goal difference and even a play-off to sort out who comes out on top! What is certain is that there's still everything to play for . . .

Leading Cup scorers

3 – Aldrin (Riverside)
2 – Pires (Kingsway Green)

MORE PROBLEMS

... Dan's still up to his tricks, on and off the pitch, but Mr Griffiths has more things to worry about than the antics of one troublesome defender ...

'What do you mean, you won't be able to play against Kingsway Green?'

'I'm sorry, Mr Griffiths, but my mother is getting married that day.'

'Your *mother*?'

Adam Trent shuffled his feet in embarrassment. 'Yes, my parents got divorced, see, and now Mum's getting married again,' he explained. 'And I've only just realized the wedding is on the same day as the match. I mean, I'd rather play football but, well, you know ...'

'OK, thanks for letting me know, Adam. I understand,' the teacher sighed as the boy tailed off. 'I guess we'll just have to play somebody else in goal and hope for the best.'

Adam disappeared quickly, glad to escape. He'd thought that Mr Griffiths might be mad at him. Now he just had to choose the right time to tell his teammates. He didn't expect them to be as sympathetic.

Mr Griffiths walked thoughtfully into the staffroom, where he found the head of the P.E. department, Mrs Thompson, waiting for him. 'Ah, glad to catch you, Doug,' she began. 'I'm afraid we've hit a problem.'

'Not another one!' he groaned. 'My Year Seven goalie has just informed me that he can't play in our next Cup game.'

'Oh, dear! That makes things even worse. I don't quite know the best way to break this to you, but he's not the only one. There's a fixture clash.'

'Wait, let me guess. You want Emerson Marshall to wear a skirt and turn out for your netball team,' he said sarcastically.

Mrs Thompson pulled a face. 'Don't be like that, Doug. I've just heard that the Quarter cross-country championships have been cancelled because of all the rain. The course at Medford is still waterlogged.'

'So? How does that affect the County Cup?'

'They've been switched to Saturday, the sixth of December.'

'What!' he gasped. 'Come off it, Val. You're joking, aren't you?'

'I'm afraid not. There are hundreds of children of all ages taking part from dozens of schools.

Very few of them will be involved in the County Cup.'

'But three of my footballers are in the cross-country team.'

She nodded. 'Sorry – but I still want them to run.'

'Can't we give them a choice?' he asked in desperation, knowing what the answer would be. Mrs Thompson was very keen on the school winning more cross-country cups to put in the trophy cabinet.

'No, I don't think so. Some of these boys have to learn that there's more to life than just football.'

'They won't like it when they find out,' he warned her miserably.

'Maybe not, but I know they enjoy their running too,' she said. 'I'm sure you can manage without them for one day. And at least you've got Dan Cross back in action again now.'

That remark did nothing to cheer him up. 'No

Adam,' he muttered under his breath, 'and now no Sam, no Dylan and no Kenny either. That's my sweeper system completely down the pan!'

Mr Griffiths almost found himself wishing that Dan *was* good at cross-country. 'Too much like hard work for him,' he murmured. 'The only kind of running he likes to do is away from school!'

. . . one week later . . .

Three boys sat outside the High Street fish and chip shop, waiting for it to open for lunch. Dan had persuaded Kenny and Sam to stay off school with him, both feeling resentful over the cross-country business. The truanting trio had not even bothered to go in for registration. They'd messed about in the park for a while, then wandered around a few shops, allowing the more experienced Dan to pinch some sweets for them all to share.

'It's not fair,' grumbled Kenny. 'We want to play in the Cup.'

'Good mind not to try too hard in the race now, just to get my own back on Tommo for making us miss the footie,' Sam muttered.

Dan grinned. 'I'll be thinking of you two, slogging round a great long, hilly course, up to your knees in mud and water.'

'Huh! Bet you won't,' Kenny grunted. 'You'll be too busy hacking some poor kid to bits.'

'Yeah, I'll give one or two of the Kingsway lot a couple of kicks for you. How about that? Does that make you feel any better?'

'No, it doesn't. I don't want you getting your-self sent off again, not for the school. We're gonna have to put out a weakened team as it is.'

'I'll make sure the ref don't see me.'

'Are you sure we won't get seen here?' asked Sam, looking around somewhat nervously.

'Who by?' scoffed Dan. 'If anybody asks us what we're up to, we'll just say we're doing a project. A traffic survey, that's always a good excuse. I've got a piece of paper in my pocket, just in case.'

Sam shivered. 'You said this would be a good laugh – but it's not.'

'Better than sitting in school, being bored.'

'Huh! At least we'd be *warm* and bored there instead of sitting on a cold pavement.'

'Well, OK then, better than working.' Dan scowled. 'You two are looking so guilty, you're cramping my style. I can get up to loads more things on my own.'

'Just doesn't seem right, somehow,' Kenny said. 'I mean, it's different when you're on holiday, but it feels weird being out and about like this on a normal schoolday.'

'You didn't have to come with me, y'know. Nobody forced you.'

Their absence had not gone unnoticed. Dan's form tutor had reported him missing immediately because of his reputation, while Sam and Kenny's non-appearance at a breaktime meeting about cross-country practices had alerted Mrs Thompson's suspicions. She decided to go and have a little drive around town during a late-morning free period, just on the off-chance . . .

A blue car suddenly veered to a stop in front of the three hunched figures on the kerb and the driver's window wound down. They looked up out of curiosity and then heard a familiar-sounding voice.

'Good morning, boys – having fun together, are we?' it greeted them, before adding in a more sinister tone, 'Oh, dear! Looks to me like you've just had your chips!'

. . . wonder what will happen to them now? What do you think should be done to tackle the serious problem of truancy? . . .

FLOODLIT FOOTBALL

... from floods to floodlights – Mr Riley has his area squad together for an evening practice session at an outdoor sports centre in Longby ...

'Great shot, Geoff,' called out the coach, using the boy's nickname. 'I hope you don't hit one like that when Hillcrest play Riverside in the Cup!'

Robert Hurst grinned. He hadn't yet been given a full game for the West Quarter and was keen to impress enough to be picked for Saturday's match against the South. 'Geoff' was one of several players enjoying some shooting practice at keeper Adam Trent, who clung on well to the next fizzing shot that he faced.

'Well saved, Adam,' Mr Riley praised him. 'I hear you're not able to play in your final Cup match. A bit of a blow for Mr Griffiths, that, on top of losing people to the cross-country championships as well.'

Mr Riley was trying hard to hide a smirk, relieved that none of his own regulars at Riverside were involved in the running.

'We'll be OK,' put in Iain Baxter, Adam's Westbridge teammate. 'We've got a new kid starting at the College on Monday. Must be pretty good too. He went for special coaching at a Centre of Excellence where he used to live.'

'Really? Could be a useful addition to the Quarter squad next term, by the sound of it. What's his name?'

Bax shrugged. 'Oliver something, I think. Emerson might know.'

As the area team manager wandered thoughtfully across the brightly lit all-weather surface towards where Emerson was practising, Adam and Bax exchanged grins. 'You've got him worried now,' said the goalie. 'He wants Kingsway to beat us, remember.'

Bax laughed. 'I know. Kenny told me to put the wind up him if I had the chance.'

Kenny wasn't able to attend this training session. He was serving an after-school detention with Dan and Sam as part of their punishment for playing truant.

Mr Riley watched Emerson's group in action for a while as they worked on their ball control, and then called the defender over to him. 'I gather things are so bad at Westbridge that you've had to go into the transfer market and sign up a new star player!' he said jokily.

'Oh, Oliver Yates, you mean?' Emerson replied. 'Yeah, just in time for the Cup. Mr Griffiths says he scored loads of goals for his old school.'

The next quarter of an hour was devoted to dribbling skills. Mr Riley tried to demonstrate a few tricks himself first, using Emerson and Adrian Norman as opponents. He played local football as a striker and left Big Norm in a tangle with a deft body swerve, but Emerson stepped in quicker than expected and his well-timed tackle swept the ball away. The teacher finished up on his backside – to the great delight of all the boys.

'Yes, well, that's not quite how to do it,' he said sheepishly. 'You've got to keep the ball under closer control than I did there.'

Mr Riley organized the squad into threes so that each player could have a turn at trying to dribble past the other two. 'If you manage to beat both of them, your reward is the chance to go and belt the ball into that far goal.'

The footballers did not fare much better than their coach. If they wriggled past the first tackler, the second usually managed to take the ball off them.

'Not as easy as it might look, is it?' he laughed. 'I want to see quick feet and sudden changes of pace to fool the defenders. Some of you are what I call "playground dribblers" – head down and charge straight on. You need to look up more.'

Captain Robbo proved the most successful performer. In his final turn he nutmegged Buzz and then unbalanced his best mate Illy with a subtle feint and shimmy. He darted away to score, pretending it was the winning goal in a floodlit international at Wembley.

'Yes, OK, Robbo,' chuckled Mr Riley. 'Not bad. Bet you can't go and do that against the South.'

'I'll have a go,' he promised.

The captain kept his word too. The West won

the match 2–0, with goals from Geoff and Robbo
– the second being the result of a thrilling piece
of dribbling. Robbo bamboozled three defenders,
plus the goalkeeper, before lashing the ball glee-
fully into the net.

'Practice makes perfect!' smiled Mr Riley in
satisfaction, giving a thumbs-up signal to his
celebrating players.

COUNTY COACH

DRIBBLING

A player who runs with the ball and dribbles it past opponents can be very exciting to watch. Sometimes the ball is lost, but a pacy dribble can also create openings for goals to be scored.

Want to improve your own dribbling skills? Take a few tips from me.

✓ Keep ball close to your feet – use quick, short taps
✓ Keep well balanced over the ball as you move
✓ Use both feet – inside and outside of the boot
✓ Use slalom course to practise dribbling round obstacles
✓ Gradually increase speed as ball control improves
✓ Don't just look down at the ball – head up and look around
✓ Unbalance opponent by sudden changes of pace and direction
✓ Accelerate away when opponent is beaten – no need to beat him twice
✓ Practise body swerves and feints to trick opponents
✓ Study good dribblers and try to copy their tricks
✓ Keep practising

MAGIC DRIBBLE!

WHO'S PLAYING?

... after a Wednesday lunchtime practice session in the new sports hall at Westbridge, Mr Griffiths seeks his captain's help in selecting the Cup team ...

'So what do you think of Oliver now we've seen him in action?'

'Magic!' Emerson enthused. 'He's got skill and pace. And he's strong – not easy to knock off the ball – as I've just found out.'

The teacher smiled. 'He did look quite a handful. Shall we risk putting him straight in the team on Saturday? I know he's keen to play.'

'No risk,' said Emerson. 'We need him in attack.'

'Agreed. Right, that's one less problem. Now, who's going to take Adam's place – Bax or Jacob?'

'Seems a shame to waste Bax in goal. He's better at scoring goals than stopping them.'

'Hmm, I take your point, but he's probably got a safer pair of hands than Jacob.'

'You mean, the way Jacob just let that shot go in through his legs?' Emerson grinned.

'Exactly. We can do without conceding a daft

goal like that in the Cup. It's a tricky decision to make. It might depend how we line up. With Kenny out, we'll have to scrap the sweeper system and perhaps play 4–3–3 instead.'

'We could just have three at the back, and use Dan and Craig as wing-backs,' Emerson suggested after consideration. 'Dan *is* playing, isn't he?'

'As long as he doesn't get involved in any more nonsense between now and Saturday,' replied Mr Griffiths with a sigh. 'But it's too late to switch to wing-backs. They'd need more time to get used to new roles like that.'

Emerson nodded, accepting that the teacher was right. 'Er, I've got to go and get changed, Mr Griffiths. The bell will be going soon.'

'Oh, yes, sorry. Just wanted to see what you thought – thanks. Tell the others I'll put the team up on the board tomorrow and we'll have our usual meeting Friday break, OK? Off you go.'

There was a scramble to read the teamsheet before morning registration next day. The names were neatly printed out from a computer as usual, along with details about times and appeals for help with transport to Kingsway Green. Bax was not too pleased to see his name underneath the number one shirt.

Team (4–3–3 formation)

1

Iain Baxter

2	5	6	3
Dan Cross	Emerson Marshall	Brad Gibson	Craig Dalton
	(captain)		

4	8	10
Eddie Atkins	Richard Congdon	Andy Thornton

7	9	11
Ajay Jethwa	Oliver Yates	Yagnesh Sharma

Subs: Jacob Roberts, Mark Palmer, Dean Matthews

... the stage is now set for the final simultaneous games, so remind yourself of the group table positions, if need be – then imagine you're sitting in front of two screens, switching attention from one to the other, so that you can follow the action from both venues ... as it happens ...

HILLCREST v RIVERSIDE

Saturday 6 December
k.o. 10 a.m.
Referee: Mr P. Wilson

. . . Hillcrest's third home game in succession in the County Cup, but their only hope of qualification now is a big win . . .

The Sky-Blues make the kind of start they must have dreamt about.

In Hillcrest's first attack of the game, captain Rafiq whips a low cross into the goalmouth from the right wing and Scott Gilbert turns the ball into the net.

'Concentrate!' Mr Wilson calls out before the restart. 'We scored first in both the other games, remember. Good teams don't keep throwing away leads.'

★ *Score-check: Hillcrest 1–0 Riverside*

KINGSWAY GREEN v WESTBRIDGE

Saturday 6 December
k.o. 10 a.m.
Referee: Mr D. Harris

. . . the first fifteen minutes here are a goal-less stalemate, but things liven up when Dan Cross tries to kick Didier Pires halfway back to France . . .

'Penalty!'
The loud appeal from the home players and supporters is perfectly synchronized. Only Didier fails to join in. He's too busy rolling about on the ground, holding his leg in pain.

'What did you go and do that for?' Emerson complains bitterly. 'He wasn't going to score from that angle.'

'Can't stand Frogs,' Dan sneers. 'Don't panic. Bax'll save it.'

Bax is more used to taking penalties than facing them. It feels weird to see the situation from the goalkeeper's point of view. He decides

In order to finish top of the group, the red-shirted visitors know they have to get a better result this morning than their main rivals, Westbridge. The Riverside players have never seen Mr Riley so agitated. As they struggle to find their form after the early shock, he scampers up and down the touchline as if wanting to join in and have a few kicks himself.

'Use the wings, Reds,' he bellows. 'Get it out to Tom – he's in loads of space.'

The teacher is so used to making space jokes about Armstrong and Aldrin that the connection comes naturally by now. But he's right on this occasion. Hillcrest's full-back, Hywel, is giving Thomas Armstrong too much space to run at him.

Illy makes the defender pay the price for such loose marking, sliding the ball perfectly into the winger's flightpath. The number eleven, starting only his second game for Riverside, takes Hywel on at speed and cuts inside before hitting a left-footed shot from the edge of the penalty area.

Struck with the outside of the boot, the ball curls wide of the goalkeeper's dive and seems to be flying wide of the far post too, until it swings late and slaps high into the roof of the net. A spectacular goal!

to stand on his line just to the left of centre. 'Think I'll try and make him hit it to my right – he won't be able to resist a gap like that.'

Captain Kyle Richards takes the responsibility for the spot-kick on his own shoulders.

The keeper sways his arms to and fro, edging his feet back towards the centre of the goal, ready to dive. Kyle spots the slight movement and, as he makes contact with the ball, places it to Bax's left instead. Bax sprawls on the ground empty-handed and doesn't even see the ball sail wide of the opposite post.

'Great stuff, Bax!' Dan whoops in relief, running to help his mate up. 'You made him change his mind at the last second.'

The stunned Kyle soon feels even worse. Westbridge go straight down the other end and show him how to put the ball in the back of the net.

Oliver Yates has made a quiet start to the game, looking a little nervous, but he now gives a glimpse of his true talents. He outjumps the tall centre-back for a cross and heads the ball down to Yagnesh, who strikes it first time past the gawping Gary in goal.

★ **Score-check: Kingsway Green 0–1 Westbridge**

A jubilant Thomas continues his run round the back of the goal and then dances along the opposite touchline.

'Good job Tom wasn't doing cross-country this morning,' chuckles Mr Riley. 'If he won his race, he'd have probably charged off on a lap of honour round the course again!'

 Score-check: Hillcrest 1–1 Riverside

The teams are locked at 1–1 for most of the rest of the half, but with Riverside's Marty Gayle much the busier of the two goalkeepers. He excels himself with one reflex save, tipping a snapshot from BB round the post. Marty can't prevent the striker's next effort from going in, though. BB plays a quick one-two with Geoff Hurst and then slips a shot beyond the goalie's reach into the bottom corner of the net.

Hillcrest deserve to be ahead on the balance of play, but everyone is well aware that their fate isn't entirely in their own hands. As the boys slurp on juicy slices of orange during the interval, the other thing on their lips is the question: 'Wonder what's happening further south?'

Half-time score: Hillcrest 2–1 Riverside

Oliver has suddenly caught fire. A minute later he's faster off the mark than anybody else to react to a rebound off a defender's leg, but puts his effort a fraction wide of the post.

'Should have been two!' he screams in frustration at his own miss. 'That was rubbish!'

Few observers would guess that Westbridge are fielding an under-strength team, the way they knock the ball about confidently in the closing stages of the first half. The next goal seems only a matter of time away, but when it arrives it proves to be a surprise equalizer for Kingsway Green.

It's the result of a series of mistakes. King Kong fouls Callum clumsily in midfield and the quick free-kick catches the Westbridge defence napping. The marking is slack for once, allowing Didier time and space to turn and shoot at goal. He hits the shot right at the keeper, but Bax fumbles the ball and Kyle gratefully accepts the chance to atone for his penalty miss by stabbing it over the line.

Half-time score: Kingsway Green 1–1 Westbridge

They find out the answer shortly before the second half gets underway. As arranged, teachers at Kingsway Green High and Hillcrest Comprehensive have been in touch by phone to swap the latest scores.

'One-all there, is it?' repeats Robbo, the Riverside captain. 'OK, let's hope it stays like that. If Westbridge only draw, any kind of win will do us.'

'Yeah, but we're losing,' Illy points out.

'We can soon put that right,' Robbo insists. 'And when Westbridge find out we're losing, they might just play for a draw – y'know, thinking they only need a point to qualify.'

Mr Riley cuts across them. 'You can go round in circles working out all the ifs and maybes,' he says. 'We've got no control over what might be going on there. Forget about Westbridge and keep your mind on trying to win this match. That's all we can do.'

Footballers are not always even in control over what happens in their own game. Fortune also plays its part, as is illustrated midway through the second half when both sides hit the post in quick succession. One shot ricochets away to safety, the other deflects into the net.

'Great! Riverside are losing,' cheers Yagnesh when the 2–1 scoreline is relayed by phone from Longby. 'A draw might be good enough after all.'

'Huh! A draw! We can beat this lot dead easy,' Dan scoffs.

'Might help if you don't give any more penalties away,' says Emerson.

'He missed it, didn't he?'

The captain grimaces. 'Just cut out all the rough stuff, OK? And the same with you, King Kong. We're giving away too many free-kicks.'

Kingsway Green also take encouragement from events further away. They know that if they can pull off a victory, they might yet retain the Shield.

'There it is,' Mr Harris says, pointing to the trophy on a nearby table. 'It's waiting for you people to reclaim it.'

It serves as excellent motivation and Didier fires the first warning shot of the second half that the holders aren't going to release their grip on the Shield without a fight. His volley from the left-hand edge of the area skims narrowly over the bar, with Bax making only a token gesture of diving for it.

 Score-check: Kingsway Green 1–1 Westbridge

Overlapping up the right wing for Hillcrest, Hywel thumps a terrific drive against the woodwork only to see Riverside break away from the rebound and launch a raid of their own. Buzz Aldrin finishes it off in deadly fashion. His measured, side-foot shot clips the inside of a post and bounces across the line to nestle in the opposite corner of the goal.

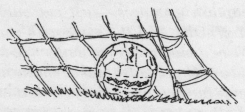

★ *Score-check: Hillcrest 2–2 Riverside*

If this stroke of bad luck isn't enough to dash Hillcrest's hopes of laying the Cup ghosts from the past, then the next blow certainly is. Just five minutes later, goalkeeper Sam does well to parry a close-range shot from Buzz, but Robbo stretches out a leg to knock the ball home.

The captain leaps high with excitement. 'Yeesss!' he shrieks. 'That's it! We've done it.'

★ *Score-check: Hillcrest 2–3 Riverside*

Dan takes up the challenge. Viewing the talented, long-haired number ten as the main threat, the defender decides to deal with him personally. Didier doesn't even see what hits him. As he trots towards the halfway line, an opponent brushes by and swings an elbow back into his face. It's only as the ball is cleared that people realize that a player is lying on the pitch in a crumpled heap.

'What happened, Didier?' asks the referee, helping him to sit up and wiping away a smear of blood from around his nose. 'Who did it?'

Didier gives his version of the Gallic shrug, but neither of them needs three guesses as to the culprit. Mr Harris glares at Dan but has no proof to take any action. The boy has been too sly.

The game becomes increasingly scrappy and ill-tempered, with an outbreak of petty fouls.

Westbridge are by far the worst offenders, targeting Kingsway Green's skilful midfielders, but some of the home players also start seeking retaliation and the referee is in danger of losing control.

★ ***Score-check: Kingsway Green 1–1 Westbridge***

↓

Mr Riley tries to calm his players down. 'It's not over yet. We need another goal to make sure, in case Westbridge snatch a winner,' he warns, disregarding his previous advice. 'Go for a fourth.'

He doesn't need to explain more. He's made the players fully aware of the mathematics involved. Even if the schools finish level on points and with the same goal difference, Riverside could still take the title through scoring a higher number of goals.

Hillcrest only have their pride to play for now. They don't want to suffer another home defeat, or to let Riverside use them for shooting practice. Rafiq won't allow any of his teammates' heads to drop and drives them forward with stubborn determination.

'Let's get that equalizer,' he demands. 'Don't let these guys walk all over us.'

. . . it's amazing how many matches are decided in the last few minutes – and this one is no exception . . .

↓

Then comes a bombshell from Longby. The shock news that Riverside have just gone ahead jolts Mr Griffiths into taking long-overdue action to try and improve the standard of the College's football.

'Might be a bit risky,' he thinks, 'but – win or lose – I reckon it's time for some drastic changes round here.'

The most persistent foulers, Dan and King Kong, are both substituted, and Bax is restored to his normal position to bolster the attack. Jacob Roberts swiftly pulls on the team's red goalie top for the first time and Bax is delighted to swap it for a white one again.

'C'mon, we need a goal,' shouts their leading scorer. 'Give me the ball.'

. . . is the gamble going to pay off or have Westbridge left it too late? The referee has already had a glance at his watch . . .

Final minutes

Riverside are pressed back on the defensive, desperate to protect their lead, despite their intentions of adding to it.

As they resort to kicking the ball anywhere to use up extra seconds, Marty is called upon to make the save of the game as he clings on to a scorching volley from Scott.

'Keep this thing up the other end,' cries the goalie, booting the ball away upfield. 'I don't want to have to touch it again.'

Only half his wish is granted. The ball is soon back in his own penalty area, but this time he doesn't lay a glove on it. Geoff's explosive shot bounces back out of the net before Marty even makes a move. The ball has come through a ruck of players in front of the goalie and he has no time to react. He simply stares at his team-mates, open-mouthed and helpless.

'A draw might still be enough,' Illy murmurs, clutching at straws. 'So long as Westbridge lose . . .'

Result:	Hillcrest	3 v 3	Riverside
		h-t: 2– 1	
Scorers:	Gilbert, Boswell		Armstrong
	Hurst		Aldrin, Robson

KINGSWAY GREEN v WESTBRIDGE

Final minutes

Jacob does not have to wait very long for his first touch. The stopgap keeper is soon forced to scuttle across his line to push the ball round the post. It's a vital save, but not as good as his next. The corner falls to Callum and his shot looks goalbound until the ball is spectacularly plucked out of the air.

'Total respect, man,' Emerson grins, hauling Jacob back to his feet.

With two weary teams going all out for a winning goal, however, the deadlock at last is broken. Bax hooks a hopeful cross into the middle towards the only other white shirt he can see – the one worn by Oliver Yates.

The debutant striker shoots on the run with ferocious power. Oliver starts to celebrate even before the ball rockets past Gary's despairing dive.

It's a quality goal. But as his delirious teammates mob the scorer, they still don't know for sure whether it has won them the West Quarter Shield.

Result:	Kingsway Green	1 v 2	Westbridge
	h-t: 1 – 1		
Scorers:	Richards		Sharma
			Yates

87

AFTERMATH

. . . a post-match telephone call confirms the two results for all concerned . . .

—at Longby:

'I just don't believe it,' murmured Robbo, slumped in a corner of the quiet changing room, totally drained of emotion. 'After all that effort. I really thought this was going to be our year to win the Cup.'

Rafiq was sitting next to his area team captain. 'So did we,' he replied wistfully. 'Hoped it would be, anyway, if only to shut Willy up.'

'Willy?'

'Yeah, the ref,' he said, nodding towards Mr Wilson. 'We're fed up with hearing about the time he won the Cup.'

'When was that?' asked Robbo, surprised.

'Oh, yonks ago. I reckon he must have a degree in ancient history.'

Robbo managed to raise a little smile. 'It wouldn't have mattered in the end if you *had* beaten us today, what with Westbridge winning as well.'

'True – and the same for you lot.'

'Not if we'd won by a couple of goals,' Robbo sighed.

The two teachers had been doing their best to console the players, but Mr Riley decided it was time for everyone to stop moping. 'OK, lads, get changed now and let's go home,' he told them. 'I guess it just wasn't meant to be our day.'

—at Kingsway Green:

'We've done it! We've won the group!' cried Emerson, jumping up and down on the pitch when they heard the final score from Longby. He made no pretence of staying cool. 'We're in the semis now.'

Dan remained aloof from the Westbridge celebrations. 'Might just play for Wanderers after Christmas,' he muttered to himself as nobody else wanted to listen to his moans. 'I've had a right bellyful of old Griff subbing me. His loss, not mine.'

Kingsway Green quickly came to terms with their own disappointment, but they still looked on in envy as Emerson strode forward to receive the West Quarter Shield. The captain brandished the trophy high in the air and gave his father a big grin.

'Dad can sing Bob Dylan all the way home now if he wants to,' he decided.

'Well done, everybody,' Mr Griffiths praised them after the presentation ceremony was over. 'Not bad for a team that had to play all their Cup games away from home.'

Dan was the only one not smiling as the players clustered together to hold up their winners' medals in front of parents' clicking cameras.

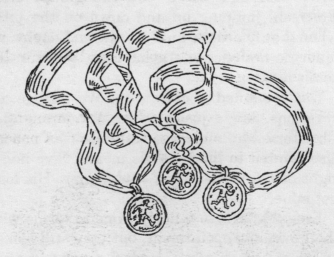

POSTSCRIPT

. . . it's the last day of term and some eagerly-awaited information has been faxed through to Westbridge Community College – the draw for the semi-finals of the County Cup . . .

Emerson led the stampede of footballers towards the P.E. block. 'Griff said he's just pinned up the draw,' he shouted to anybody he saw on the way across the playground. 'C'mon, let's see who we've got.'

The group skidded to a halt in front of the overcrowded sports noticeboard outside the boys' changing room.

'Where is it?' cried Bax.

'There – look!' exclaimed Emerson, stabbing a long finger at the all-important sheet of paper. 'It's Glendale in the North!'

'Wonder how good Glendale really are?' said Kenny, the new West Quarter under-12 cross-country champion. 'We must've played against a few of their guys in that area match.'

'What was the score against the North?' asked Sam.

'Drew three-all,' answered Adam, pulling a face at the memory. 'I let two stupid goals in that day.'

'Just as well we've got Jacob, then, to take your place so it won't happen again,' Emerson teased him.

'Watch it! Don't be cheeky,' the goalkeeper grinned back.

Dan strolled up at that moment. 'Who is it, then?' he said casually, not making any effort to look at the notice himself.

'Thought you weren't interested,' the captain replied, testing him out. 'You told me you weren't playing for the College again.'

Dan shrugged. 'Might do. Have to see how I feel.'

'Have to see whether you bother to turn up, you mean.'

'It's Glendale,' Sam put in before Dan could react to the taunt. 'We're at home in the first leg.'

'Glendale? Never heard of 'em,' Dan snorted. 'And where's the home game gonna be played, anyway? On one of our chewed-up mudheaps?'

The others hadn't really given that matter too much thought as yet. They'd only played one match at home all term, and that was on a newly created, swampy pitch at the furthest corner of the playing fields. Kenny had scored with a shot from inside his own half, the pitch was so short.

'That little pitch is no good for the County Cup,' said Emerson, 'and the main pitch is too big for people our age.'

'They can't expect us to play both legs at Glendale,' muttered King Kong. 'That wouldn't be fair.'

Yagnesh spoke up hesitantly. 'Er, suppose I should have said something about this before, but I'm not sure I'll be here to play in the first leg now I've seen the date.'

Everyone looked at him. 'What d'yer mean?' demanded Bax.

He sighed. 'Well, my parents are taking me to India in the New Year to show me where they were born. We're going to stay with relatives I've never even met.'

'How long are you going to be away for?' asked Emerson, alarmed at the prospect of losing their goalscoring midfielder.

'About a month or so, I think. Don't really want to go, but I've got no choice. You know how it is . . .'

'Does Griff know about this?'

Yagnesh gave a little shrug. 'I haven't told him, but my parents have got permission from the College for my absence. I just didn't realize the trip would clash with the Cup. Sorry . . .'

They were all sorry. Their semi-final seemed to be hitting problems already – before a ball was even kicked.

. . . wonder how Westbridge will tackle the problems over players and pitches after Christmas? Sounds like more headaches for Mr Griffiths!

Find out what happens in their Cup semi-final with Glendale in Book 6 of the series . . .

APPENDIX

Hillcrest	1 v 1	Kingsway Green
Riverside	2 v 2	Westbridge
Hillcrest	1 v 3	Westbridge
Kingsway G	2 v 3	Riverside
Hillcrest	3 v 3	Riverside
Kingsway G	1 v 2	Westbridge

FINAL GROUP TABLE

	P	W	D	L	Goals F	A	(GD)	Pts
Westbridge	3	2	1	0	7	4	(+3)	7
Riverside	3	1	2	0	8	7	(+1)	5
Hillcrest	3	0	2	1	5	7	(−2)	2
Kingsway Green	3	0	1	2	4	6	(−2)	1

GOALS

A total of 24 goals were scored in the six group matches, averaging four goals a game. These were the goalscorers for each school:

HILLCREST

2 – Hurst, Boswell

1 – Gilbert

KINGSWAY GREEN

2 – Pires, Richards

RIVERSIDE

4 – Aldrin

2 – Robson

1 – Norman, Armstrong

WESTBRIDGE

2 – Sharma

1 – Baxter, Congdon, Lucas, Small, Yates